Gg Hh Ii Jj Kk Ll Mm

Uu Vv Ww Xx Yy Zz

Dear Parent,

The My First Steps to Reading® series is based on a teaching activity that helps children learn to recognize letters and their sounds. The use of predictable language patterns and repetition of familiar words will also help your child build a basic sight vocabulary. Your child will enjoy watching the characters in the books place imaginative objects in "letter boxes." You and your child can even create and fill your own letter box, using stuffed animals, cut-out pictures, or other objects beginning with the same letter. The things you can do together are limited only by your imagination. Learning letters will be fun—the first important step on the road to reading.

The Editors

All Rights Reserved. Published by Scholastic Inc., 90 Old Sherman Turnpike, Danbury, Connecticut 06810, by arrangement with The Child's World, Inc.
Scholastic offers a varied selection of children's book racks and tote bags. For details about ordering, please write to: Scholastic At Home, 90 Old Sherman Turnpike, Danbury, CT 06810, Attention: Premium Department

Originally published as *My "x, y, z" Sound Box* by The Child's World, Inc.

My First Steps to Reading is a registered trademark of Grolier Publishing Co. Inc.
SCHOLASTIC and associated logos are trademarks and/or registered trademarks of Scholastic Inc.

Printed in the U.S.A.

My "x, y, z" Book

written by Jane Belk Moncure

illustrated by Colin King

Little  X had a box.

"I will find things that begin with my letter," he said.

"I will put them into my sound  box."

Little  found an

X-ray machine.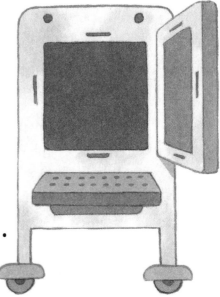

"Excellent," said Little  .

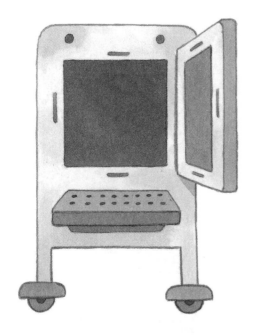

"With my X-ray machine,
I can see inside things."

"I will take an X ray of my hands."

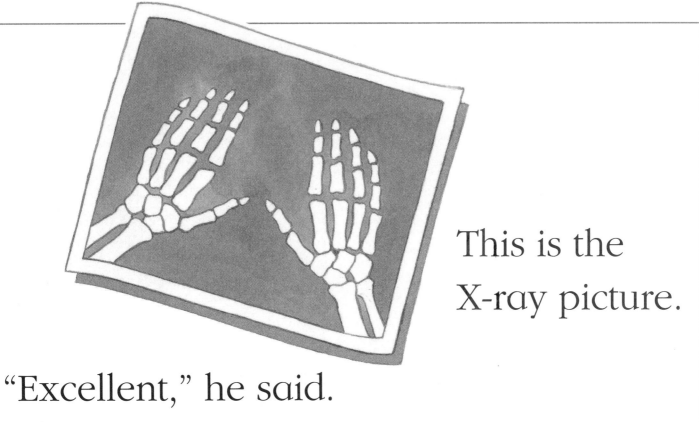

This is the
X-ray picture.

"Excellent," he said.
"The X ray shows the
bones in my hands."
He put the picture
into his sound box.

"I will take an
X ray of my feet,"
he said.

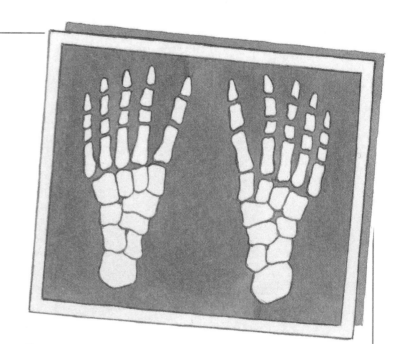

This is the X-ray picture.

"Excellent," said Little X .
"The X ray shows the
bones in my feet."

Then he put the X-ray picture
and the X-ray machine

into his sound box.

He said, "Now I will call my friend . . .

Little  ."

"I will see if he has a  box."

"I do," said Little y .

"I will find something that begins with my 'y' sound."

"I will put it into my sound box."

Little found a yo-yo.

It was a yellow yo-yo.

He tried to make the yo-yo go

down . . . . and . . . up.

But the string was too short.

Little  found some yarn.

He tied it to the string.

The yellow yo-yo went

down.

The yellow yo-yo
went up.

Little  turned his box upside down.

He stood on his box
with the yo-yo.

He said, "Now I will
call my friend . . .

Little  and see if she has

a 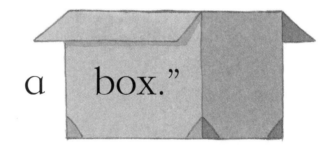 box."

"I do," said Little .

"I will find things that begin with my 'z' sound.

I will put them into my sound  box."

She found a zebra . . .

and another zebra

and another zebra.

Little  caught the three

zebras

and . . .

tried to put them into her box.

But the zebras jumped out of the box!

Zip!

Zip!

Zip!

They ran

zigzag

down the road.

"I will catch you, zippy zebras!"
called Little   .

And she did.

Then she took the zebras to the zoo.

In this story, Little **X** placed the letter "X" in front of the word "ray" to make the word "X ray."

But in some words, Little x has the "z" sound. Can you read this word with the "z" sound?

xylophone

Can you read these words with Little  ?

yard

yak

yacht

Can you read these words with Little z ?

zinnia

zip

zero

Aa Bb Cc Dd Ee Ff

Nn Oo Pp Qq Rr Ss Tt

My First Steps to READING®